Disney

HIGH SCHOOL MUSICAL

PaRragon

Bath · New York · Singapore · Hong Kong · Cologne · Delhi · Melbourne

GET'CHA HEAD IN THE GAME

First published by Parragon in 2008
Parragon
Queen Street House
4 Queen Street
Bath BA1 1HE, UK

ISBN 978-1-4075-1734-6

Printed in China

ALL ABOUT ME!

Write as much as you can about yourself on this page!

My NAME Beth Wilson

My HEIGHT

My FAVOURITE COLOUR Red

My SHOE SIZE 3 or 4

My DATE OF BIRTH 29/09/98

My EYE COLOUR bluey Grey

My FAVOURITE BAND Abba + Alphabeat + Greenday

My FAVOURITE HSM SONG all in this together

Stick in a picture of yourself, your house or anything you can think of that best describes you!

My **ADDRESS:**
4 Hill view place Fallin
FK7 7JS

My **FAVOURITE HOBBIES:**
Singing, dancing, acting + swimming + skipping

SCRAPBOOKING!

A **SCRAPBOOK** is an album that you create,
which is
ALL ABOUT YOU!

Use it to write down:
YOUR THOUGHTS
SECRET AMBITIONS
BEST FRIENDS
HOBBIES
and **ACHIEVEMENTS**.

Every character in **HIGH SCHOOL MUSICAL** is
different. **CHAD** likes to play sports and **TAYLOR**
is a serious brainiac. **SHARPAY** is a drama queen and
TROY and **GABRIELLA** are true stars! You're unique
too, so use this book to explain how!

Use this scrapbook to tell **YOUR OWN STORY!**
Once you've finished the book, you'll have
a one-of-a-kind treasury of things all about you!

There's no right or wrong way to create a scrapbook
- it's your book to create in any way you want.
GO WILD!

GO WILDCATS

CHAD

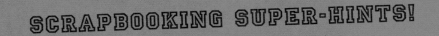

SCRAPBOOKING SUPER-HINTS!

Stick anything you can think of into your scrapbook to help you personalize the book as much as possible.

Did you receive any funny or super-cute birthday cards this year? Cut them out and tape them in!

TOP TIPS:
A solid glue stick is the best thing to use in your scrapbook.
Use your groovy **HIGH SCHOOL MUSICAL** tapes provided to stick things in!

HSM

Been to any great films at the cinema recently? Stick in your cinema tickets!

Flown to any exotic countries? Keep your plane tickets in the specially designed scrapbook pocket!

You could glue in scraps of material to help you design costumes.

MORE ABOUT ME!

Use these pages to stick in pictures of all of your friends, family and pets. Write about them underneath their pictures!

All about this photo...

My best friend...
Chelsea Walker

How long have you known all of your friends for? How did you meet?

Me and my friends together...
We go to the cinema

What do your mum and dad do for a living?

My mum works in a post Office and my dad works at Stirling Precast

Do you have any brothers or sisters?
What are their names and how old are they?

none (yes!)

WILDCATS
14
ATHLETIC DEPT.

All about this photo...

My family...

MORE FACTS ABOUT ME!

My favourite pop band...

Alphabeat
Abba

Glue in a magazine cutting
or write about your
favourite song.

My favourite food...

Steak!

Draw a picture, stick in a wrapper
or write about it!

WILDCATS BASKETBALL

The best place I ever went on holiday was...

Malta

Troy and Gabriella met on a skiing holiday. Write about your dream holiday here.

My favourite thing about High School Musical is...

The next few pages of this book are dedicated to creating your very own stage show. Take the lead from the **HIGH SCHOOL MUSICAL** gang and put on your own play!

CREATE YOUR OWN ...

You don't have to have a stage or a large theatre to put on a play.

Get your friends and family to play the parts that you write.

Who would you like to take part in your show?

....
....
....
....
....
....

Perform the play in your living room, your garden, the school playground - anywhere you can think of!

Where would be a good place to stage your show?

back Garden
....
....
....
....
....

TROY

... STAGE SHOW!

First things first, you need to write a story.
Will it be a love story, comedy or even a tragedy?
Write down all of your plot and character ideas here...

The play's title...

DESIGN YOUR ...

Right, you've got your storyline and characters decided. Now think about what each character is going to wear. Use these pages to design costumes for your play.

Glue in scraps of materials or pictures of how you'd like the characters to look.

Character's Name

....

Character's Name

....

... OWN COSTUMES!

Character's Name

....

Character's Name

....

SHARPAY

DESIGN YOUR ...

What will the stage set of your play look like? Use your imagination to design your dream set. You might not be able to create something so detailed in real life, so think about ways you could adapt it for your living room.

EAST HIGH RULES!

Props
we could use
in the play...

... STAGE SET!

My set...

RYAN

WRITE YOUR ...

Does listening to music inspire you to write your own songs, just like **KELSI**?

Make your play a musical, just like **TWINKLE TOWNE**, by composing music and writing lyrics for songs.

Use the space below to write lyrics for the songs in your play.

Verse
....
....
....
....
....

Chorus
....
....
....
....

Verse
....
....
....
....

Chorus
....
....
....
....

Verse
....
....
....
....

HINT:
You could use the microphone on your mobile phone to record the song that you make up, so you don't forget it.

... OWN SONGS!

MARCHING BAND

Do you know how to write music?
Use this musical score template to write your melody onto.

Title: . . . .

Words and Music by . . . .

Can you play a musical instrument, like the piano or guitar?
If you can, use them to help you write songs. If not, just make
up the melody by singing it.

PARTY PLANNING!

The best way to celebrate the first night of a play, a birthday or any kind of occasion is a **PARTY**! Use these pages to plan your perfect party.

DATE & TIME

VENUE

PARTY THEME

MUSIC to be played

FOOD

DRINKS

E·H·S

GAMES
we can
play

....
....
....
....
....
....

DREAM CELEBRITY GUESTS

....
....
....
....
....
....

My PRESENT WISHES:

....
....

WHAT I'M GOING TO WEAR:

....
....

PARTY ...

Once you've decided the details of your party, you need to invite people. Create really cool party invitations to send out to people.

You're invited to the party of:

....

to celebrate:

....

IT'S GOING TO BE THE PARTY OF THE YEAR!

Date:
....

Time:
....

Theme:
....

Use stickers, glitter, sequins, snippets of ribbon or anything else you fancy to decorate your invitations.

You could even photocopy a picture of yourself and stick it onto your invitations to make them as personal as possible.

HINT:
To make the invitations look super-funky, cut out letters from newspapers or magazines and glue them onto the invitations!

... INVITATIONS!

Create your own invitations and stick them in here!

WILDCATS

DEFENSE

FIGHT BACK!

GABRIELLA

DOODLE MANIA!

Do you find that you doodle on absolutely everything you can? Ever wondered what your doodles really say about you? Stick in your doodles here and use the helpful hints on these pages to write about what you think they mean!

FACES & PEOPLE

You're a very sociable person. You love making new friends and spending time with others.

FLOWERS

You have a gentle personality and love nature!

HOUSES

Doodling pictures of simple houses means that you have a very happy home life.

STARS

If you're someone who doodles stars, then you're a very ambitious person. You may even have ambitions to be on the stage – just like Troy or Gabriella.

CIRCLES

A circle represents the universe and everything in it. Someone who draws circles likes to think about absolutely everything!

SQUARES

You are a very formal and mathematical person. You like things neat and tidy.

WHAT ARE YOU ...

The students at **EAST HIGH** all achieve different things. **TROY** is proud to be the captain of the basketball team, **SHARPAY** is proud to have starred in so many school musicals and **TAYLOR** is the brainiest brainiac of them all!

SHOOT!

SCORE!

WIN!

List all of the achievements that you're most proud of here.

TAYLOR

... PROUD OF?

I'm proud of:
....
....

What have you done that you're proud of? Ever received a glowing school report? Do you have a picture of you competing in a race or taking part in a school play?

Stick in anything you can think of!

I'm proud of:
....
....

I'm proud of:
....
....

YOUR SECRET ...

Everyone has secret dreams and ambitions. Take Troy and Gabriella for instance, who both secretly dreamed about being in a high school musical.

Use these pages to write about what you secretly wish for, whether it's to be a famous singer, a successful writer, a doctor or even an astronaut!

If you're scared that someone might read what you write, why don't you try writing it in code? Use the code below as a guide – or even invent one of your own!

A	B	C	D	E	F	G	H	I	J	K	L	M	N	O	P	Q	R	S	T	U	V	W	X	Y	Z
1	2	3	4	5	6	7	8	9	10	11	12	13	14	15	16	17	18	19	20	21	22	23	24	25	26

... WISHES!

Where would you love to live when you grow up?

Where do you secretly dream about going on holiday?

If you could win an award what would it be?

What is your dream job?

If you could wish to meet any famous person, who would it be?

If you could star in any play or movie, what would it be?

Have you ever been lucky enough to collect a famous person's autograph? Use these pages to stick them in!

This autograph belongs to:

....

This autograph belongs to:

....

This autograph belongs to:

....

HINT:
If you don't have any famous peoples' autographs, then why don't you collect your friend's signatures? After all, you never know who's going to grow up to be the next big superstar!

This autograph belongs to:

....

DECIDE YOUR DESTINY!

Do you ever have difficulty making decisions? Like what to wear to a party or who your favourite **HIGH SCHOOL MUSICAL** character is? Use this awesome **DESTINY SHAPER** to help you make up your mind!

1
2
3
4
5

USING IT IS SIMPLE:

Firstly, you need to decide what you want to know, like what you'll be when you grow up. Then you have to write a different answer underneath each name on the Destiny Shaper.

Carefully cut out the Destiny Shaper and fold it up as instructed above.

• Put your thumbs and forefingers underneath the corners of each number.
• Choose a number, then pinch the Destiny Shaper and open and close it in each direction that many times.
• Now, choose a name.
• Look underneath that name to find out the answer to your question!

Use these templates to make as many Destiny Shapers as you like. You can use them to help you decide anything at all.

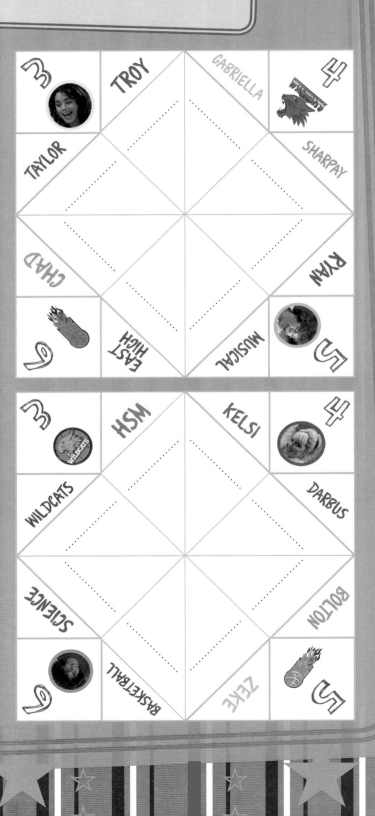

Do you find you have so many ideas to write about and pictures to stick in that you just don't have enough room?

Use these fantastic 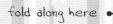 scrapbook pockets to keep things in!

Just cut out the pockets, stick them in the front and back of your HIGH SCHOOL MUSICAL scrapbook and use them to keep anything you want inside!

glue here

fold along here

fold along here

glue here

fold along here

glue here

fold along here

glue here

fold along here

fold along here

glue here

glue here